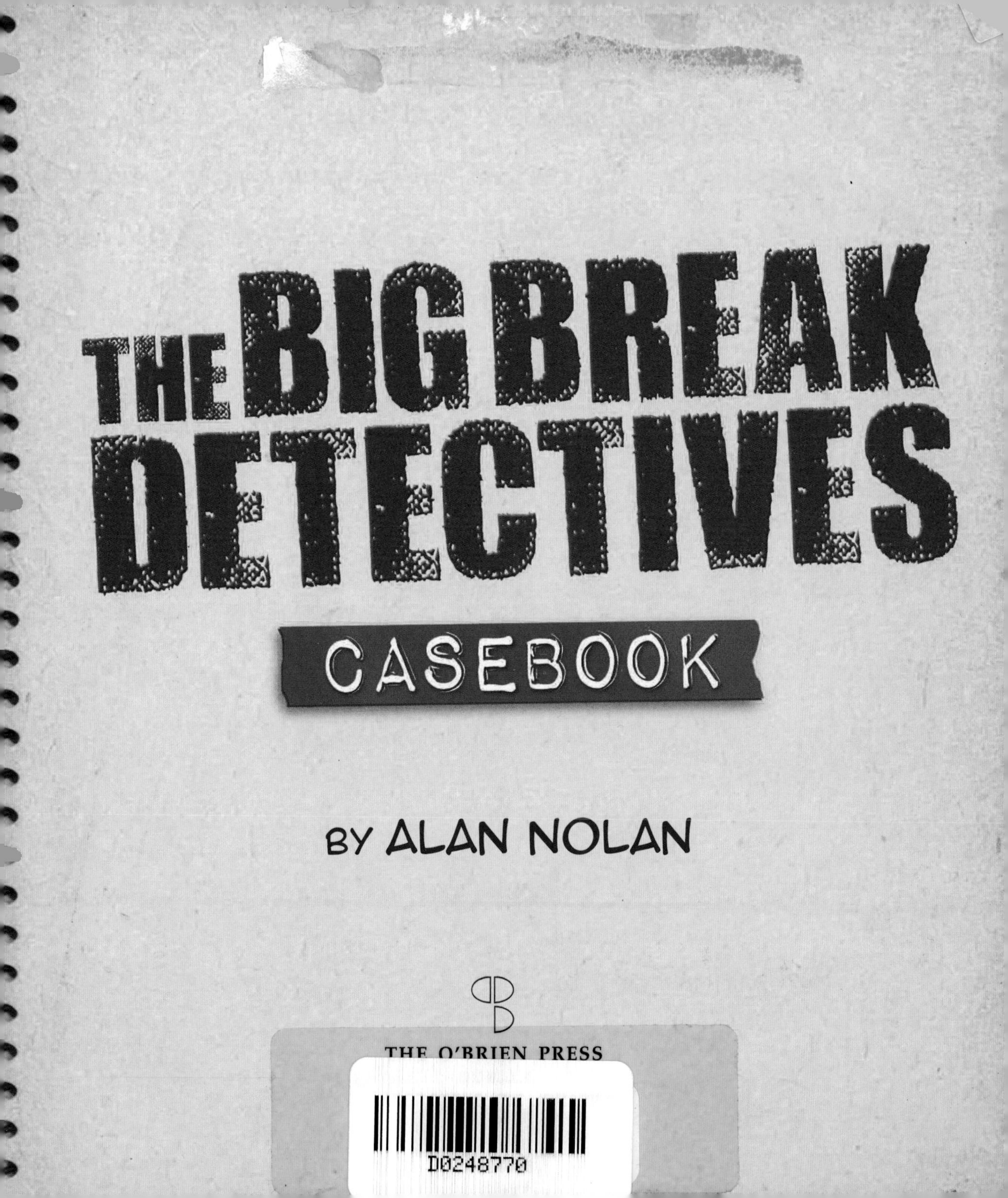
THE BIG BREAK DETECTIVES
CASEBOOK
BY ALAN NOLAN
THE O'BRIEN PRESS
D0248770

For Adam, Matthew and Sam

First published 2011 by The O'Brien Press Ltd,
12 Terenure Road East, Rathgar, Dublin 6, Ireland
Tel: +353 1 492 3333; Fax: +353 1 492 2777
Email: books@obrien.ie
Website: www.obrien.ie

Portions of this work were previously
published in RiRa comic

ISBN: 978-1-84717-252-5

A catalogue record for this title is available from the British Library

1 2 3 4 5 6
11 12 13 14

The O'Brien Press receives assistance from

Editing: The O'Brien Press Ltd
Printed and bound by KHL Printing Co Pte Ltd, Singapore

THE BIG BREAK DETECTIVES

THE CASE OF THE RUDE PARROT

case one

THE CASE OF THE RUDE PARROT

My name is Tom Conway but everyone (and I mean everyone, even my mum) calls me Little Tom.

And I am a Big Break Detective.

There's 3 of us: me, my sister Kate and our friend Danny. We're like real detectives, but we're still in school.

So we have to solve mysteries in our Big Break, and that's only 30 minutes long, so we're always in a rush!

Kate asked me to keep a journal of our adventures, so here I am. Our card:

Kate is kind of our leader, she's the brainy one.

Danny's nice, a bit sporty, if you know what I mean. Kate likes him (hee hee!) and he keeps the bullies from stealing my sweets, so I like him too.

OK, so here goes – this was one of our first cases, and I call it (because it's my journal)...

THE CASE OF THE RUDE PARROT

LADY AGATHA CHESTERTON'S SCHOOL FOR GIRLS AND BOYS, JUST BEFORE BIG BREAK.
LADY AGAT
CHESTERTO
SCHOOL FO
GIRLS & BOY
BBRRRRIIIIN NNNGGGG!
CALL
BBRRRRIIIIN NNNGGGG!
CALL
BBRRRRIIIIN NNNGGGG!
CALL
BBRRRRIIIIN NNNGGGG!
CALL
BBRRRRIIIIN NNNGGGG!
WHHIRRR!
KLIKK!

BEEP! BEEP!
ALERT! ALERT!
BEEP!
BEEP!
MISS, MAY WE GO TO THE BATHROOM?
BUT IT'S ALMOST BIG BREAK.
PLEASE MISS...
...I CAN'T WAIT!

KRASH!

CREEEAAAK!
OOF!

BBRRINNGG!

THE BIG BREAK DETECTIVES' SECRET HEADQUARTERS...
BBRRINNGG!
...90 METRES BELOW LADY AGATHA'S, 1 MINUTE LATER.
BBRRI-
HELLO? THE BIG BREAK DETECTIVES?
NO, NO, THAT'S FINE...
IGNORE ME, WHY DON'T YOU.

OH HELLO. I SAW YOUR CARD IN THE WINDOW OF THE NEWSAGENTS. "THE BIG BREAK DETECTIVES, ALL MYSTERIES SOLVED, IN 30 MINUTES, FREE OF CHARGE"?
WELL, I HAVE A MYSTERY FOR YOU!
WE'RE ON THE CASE!
MASTER TOM! DON'T FORGET THE PER-CAM!
THANKS PER-CEE -- YOU'RE THE BEST ROBO-RECEPTIONIST I KNOW.
IN FACT YOU'RE THE ONLY ONE I KNOW.
PER CEE
HUMPH. I DON'T KNOW WHY I BOTHER.
LESS THAN HALF AN HOUR, GUYS!
RUN!

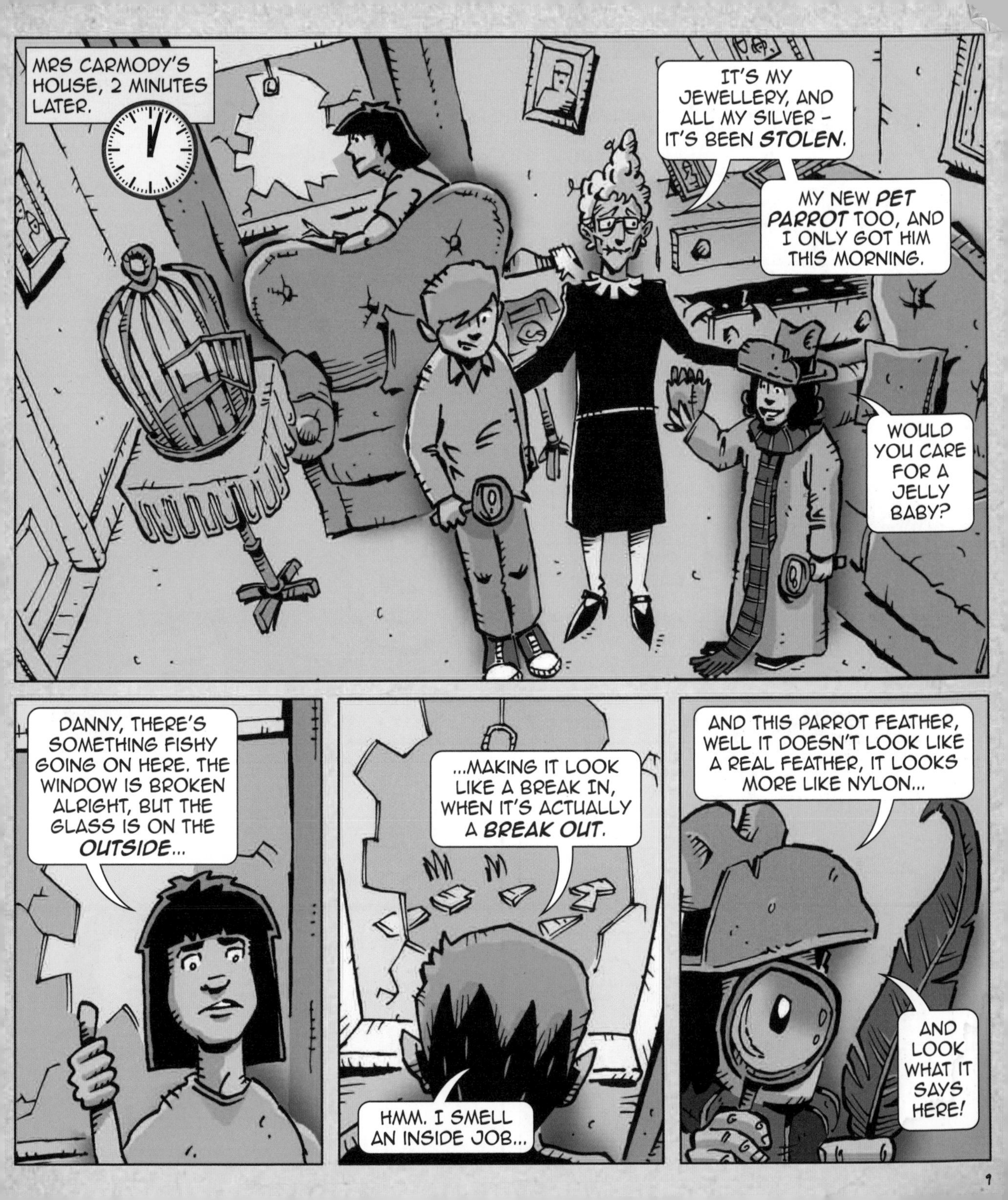
MRS CARMODY'S HOUSE, 2 MINUTES LATER.
IT'S MY JEWELLERY, AND ALL MY SILVER – IT'S BEEN STOLEN.
MY NEW PET PARROT TOO, AND I ONLY GOT HIM THIS MORNING.
WOULD YOU CARE FOR A JELLY BABY?
DANNY, THERE'S SOMETHING FISHY GOING ON HERE. THE WINDOW IS BROKEN ALRIGHT, BUT THE GLASS IS ON THE OUTSIDE...
...MAKING IT LOOK LIKE A BREAK IN, WHEN IT'S ACTUALLY A BREAK OUT.
HMM. I SMELL AN INSIDE JOB...
AND THIS PARROT FEATHER, WELL IT DOESN'T LOOK LIKE A REAL FEATHER, IT LOOKS MORE LIKE NYLON...
AND LOOK WHAT IT SAYS HERE!

MADE IN TAIWAN
MRS CARMODY, THAT PARROT YOU BOUGHT, WAS THERE ANYTHING STRANGE ABOUT IT?
WHEN I GAVE IT WATER TO DRINK IT STUCK OUT ITS TONGUE AND SAID "WATER? GIVE ME FIZZY COLA, YOU OLD BIDDY!"
IT WAS THE RUDEST PARROT I'VE EVER SEEN!
WHERE DID YOU GET IT FROM?
THERE WAS A CARD SELLING IT IN THE NEWSAGENT'S WINDOW, THE SAME PLACE I SAW YOUR CARD.
SO, WE'RE GOING TO BUY A PARROT...
AND THEN WE'LL SEE IF WE CAN MAKE IT SQUAWK!
THE NEWSAGENTS, 2 MINUTES LATER.
HERE WE ARE! PARROT FOR SALE, LARGE, GREEN AND VERY FRIENDLY - CALL SEAN TODAY!
SO CALL!
LITTLE TOM, IT'S TIME FOR YOUR EXPERT POWERS OF MIMICRY.
HUH?
PRETEND TO BE AN OLD LADY, AND SEE IF THIS SEAN GUY IS STILL SELLING THE SAME PARROT.

HELLO? I'M CALLING ABOUT THE PARROT? OH! STILL FOR SALE? OH YES, MY DEAR, PLEASE BRING IT AROUND TO MY HOUSE STRAIGHT AWAY. IT'S 222B BAKER STREET. BYE DAHLING, *BYEEE!*

Yes! I love dressing up!

my all time favourite teevee show in the whole world is "Hamm and Pickle – Masters of Disguise".

It's about two undercover cops in San Diego and in each episode they have to use their skills in dressing up and camouflage to solve the crime and catch the crook.

(You can tell every week who the crook is... it's always the special guest star).

GLOVES (RUBBER)

SWEETS (BOILED)

INNOCENT (BUT DODDERY) OLD LADY

TIGHTS (WRINKLED)

SLIPPERS (TARTAN)

...So I grabbed my handy dandy Hamm and Pickle book of brilliant disguises and thumbed my way straight to the "INNOCENT BUT DODDERY OLD LADY" section.

I don't mind Kate and Danny, but I just hope the rest of the class never see me like this...

222B BAKER STREET, 5 MINUTES LATER.
KNOCKKK!
COMING, MY DEAR!
YOUR PARROT MA'AM. THAT'LL BE 70 EURO.
OH, A BARGAIN!
JUST LEAVE IT IN THE FRONT ROOM FOR ME PLEASE, I'M GOING STRAIGHT OUT TO THE BINGO.
STRAIGHT OUT TO BINGO YOU SAY? A PLEASURE, MA'AM!
AN ABSOLUTE PLEASURE...
OW! PUT ME DOWN GENTLY, YOU EEJIT!
QUIET, YOU!

OOOOOH!
MY ACHING BACK!
DAD! DAAAAAD! THE COAST IS CLEAR!

GOOD WORK SON, I TOLD YOU THAT PARROT SCAM WOULD WORK AGAIN!
NOW, LET'S CLEAR OUT THE HOUSE WHILE THAT OLD BIDDY'S AT BINGO!
CAUGHT RED-HANDED!
AND GREEN-WINGED!
LEG IT, SON!
SQUAWK!
NOT SO FAST, YOU TWO!
POLICE
POLICE
WOULD YOU CARE FOR A LEMON SHERBET?

WELL DONE, KIDS, WE'VE BEEN AFTER THEM FOR SOME TIME.
POLICE
POLICE
POLICE
AND SPEAKING OF *TIME*...
OH! 28 MINUTES!
TIME FOR US TO MAKE LIKE PARROTS -- AND *FLY!*
BBRRINNNGG!
BBRRINNNGG!
BBRRINNNGG!
BBRRINNNGG!
BBRRINNNGG!

And that was the Case of the Rude Parrot.

We legged it back to class and we missed the whole lunch break, but at least we know that the trickster and his fine feathered son will be in an all-new cage for some time to come.

trust Diane Mulberry ... When Good Household Appliances Go Bad ... When Good Household Appliances objected to a brand new washing machine objected to the brand of fabric conditioner used and went rogue, showering her two year old daughter Isabelle with socks, trousers, jumpers and loads and loads of suds.

Absolutely hilarious.

Review

Hamm and Pickle - Masters of Disguise, Thursday

Hamm and Pickle - Masters of Disguise returned to our screens this week, and I couldn't think of a worse way to spend a Thursday night.

Wobbly sets, overacting and frankly see-through disguises are the order of the day in this clunky show which features plot holes big enough to drive Conrad Pickle's signature monster wheel pick-up truck through. (Who needs a monster wheel pick-up truck in San Diego anyway?)

Last week's episode featured a storyline which required Pickle (Salvatore Alonzo) and Hamm (Brock Gibbons) to dress up as trees. At least that suited their wooden acting style. Avoid like Dutch elm disease.

Review

Badgerwatch, Saturday

Saturday saw the welcome return of Badgerwatch, presented this time by former child star Belinda "Twinkletoes" Havisham, and she lived up to her name as she danced lightly through 2 hours of hilarious badger antics

RUBBISH!

Does this critic even OWN a TV?

That's YOUR opinion.

HAMM & PICKLE MASTERS OF DI...

THE BIG BREAK DETECTIVES

THE CASE OF THE SABOTAGED CIRCUS

The Case of the Sabotaged Circus

I don't like the circus.

I think it's the clowns that freak me out.

That and the thought of being in close proximity to wild, man-eating animals like lions, tigers and bears.

I've only ever been to the circus once when I was five. We were in the front row. A clown threw a bucket of confetti at me and I roared so much, Mum had to bring Kate and me home.

I don't think Kate has ever forgiven me.

From that day on I can't even look at a circus on teevee, and I duck down low in the back seat if Mum is driving past one.

So I was a little put out to say the least when the HQ phone rang one day...

90 METRES BELOW LADY AGATHA'S SCHOOL.
JUST 12 O'CLOCK. BIG BREAK TIME.
BBRRRIIIIN NNNGGGG!
HELLO?
YOU'RE SPEAKING TO THE BIG BREAK DETECTIVES!
AH HELLO! MY NAME IS VIVALDI AND I RUN VIVALDI'S CIRCUS --
THE ONE NEXT DOOR TO THE SCHOOL? I'M REALLY LOOKING FORWARD TO SEEING IT MR VIVALDI, I'M GOING TONIGHT!
YEAH. BY YOURSELF.
HUMPH.
I WOULD HAVE GOTTEN THAT, BUT I CAN'T REACH THE PHONE FROM HERE.
AH. THERE MAY NOT BE A SHOW TONIGHT, KIDS -- THAT'S WHY I NEED YOUR HELP!
BUT I, UM, DON'T KNOW ANYTHING ABOUT THE CIRCUS...
AW C'MON TOM, PER-CEE WILL TELL YOU ALL YOU NEED TO KNOW.
BESIDES YOU OWE ME AFTER THE CONFETTI INCIDENT.

OKAY, *OKAY*! PER-CEE, WHAT'VE YOU GOT?
OH. *NOW* I'M USEFUL.
REALLY. I DON'T KNOW *WHY* I BOTHER...
BIG TOP CIRCUS
INFO
PRESS HERE
CLOWNS
ACROBATS
ANIMALS
MUSIC
ROMAN CIRCUS
INFO
PRESS HERE
GLADIATORS
CHARIOTS
RACES
LIONS
PICCADILLY CIRCUS
INFO
PRESS HERE
LONDON
TRAFFIC
BILLBOARDS
STATUE

WE'D BETTER HURRY -- IT'S TWO MINUTES PAST 12!
RUN!
WELL, AREN'T YOU GOING? OR ARE YOU GOING TO STAY HERE MAKING THE PLACE LOOK UNTIDY?
I SUPPOSE...
AND DON'T WORRY ABOUT THE WILD ANIMALS IN THE CIRCUS. THEY WERE ONLY WILD WHEN THEY WERE CAPTURED.
YOU MEAN THAT NOW THEY'RE AT THE CIRCUS THEY'RE COMPLETELY TAME?
NO. I MEAN THAT IF THEY WERE WILD WHEN THEY WERE CAPTURED...
...THEY MUST BE ABSOLUTELY *FURIOUS* NOW!
ULP.

I suppose you're wondering how we found the HQ and met Per–cee.

You see, last year Danny and I were in detention, (don't ask, it's a long story to do with the teachers' staffroom and a badly wired, backfiring vacuum cleaner) and our punishment was to tidy up the area behind the stage in the school hall. It was very dusty and dark.

Under a grubby tarpaulin we found a broken ventilation shaft door with a ladder leading down. Danny being the bravest climbed down first and I followed. (Well, it was better than cleaning up the backstage by myself.)

At the end of the ladder we found a HUGE storeroom under the school that nobody had been in for thirty years! Every surface was covered in dust and grime.

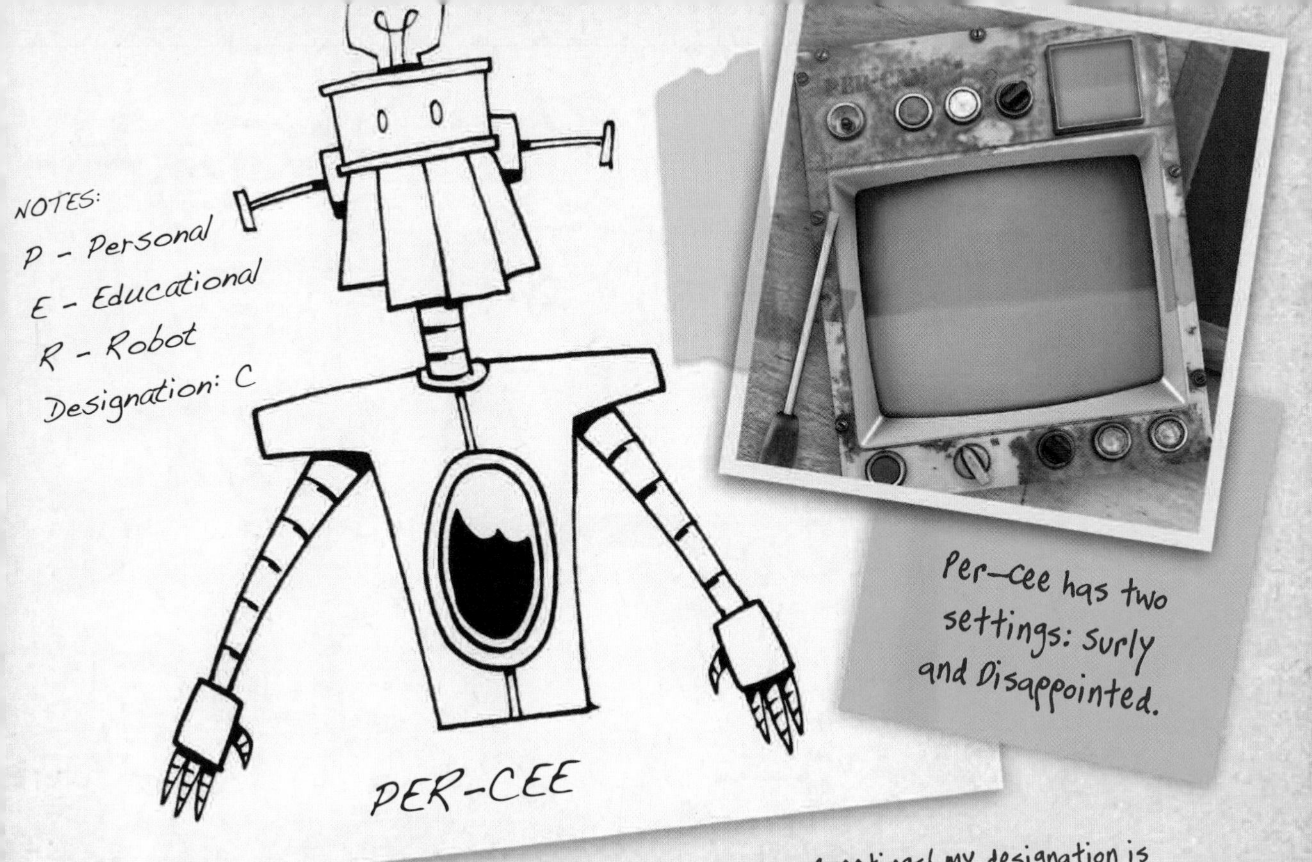

I found a light switch, and as the lights came on there were the sounds of other pieces of equipment coming to life too – clicks and whirring noises as ancient computer banks spluttered to life for the first time in years and years.

Then we heard a metallic voice behind us...

PER-CEE was built by Mr. Klamp, an old science teacher at Lady Agatha's who was an inventor in his spare time. When Mr. Klamp retired, his science lab was closed up and forgotten about.

And so was PER-CEE.

NO wonder PER-CEE's always in such bad humour...

12.03PM, THE BIG TOP, VIVALDI'S CIRCUS.
SO MR VIVALDI, WHAT CAN WE DO FOR YOU?
I THINK SOMEBODY MAY BE SABOTAGING MY CIRCUS -
IT WAS DURING REHEARSALS THIS MORNING...
HURMPH!
WOULD YOU CARE FOR A JELLY BABY?
FIRST, MY BEAUTIFUL ELEPHANT, TINY SLIPS WHILE PRACTICING HER TAPDANCE ROUTINE...
...NEXT, THE BENZINI BROTHERS FELL OFF THEIR MOTORBIKE. TWO OF THEM BRUISED THEIR EGOS, YOU KNOW.
...AND THEN THE GREAT BALLISTO'S HUMAN CANNON MISFIRED. HE CAN'T SIT DOWN FOR A WEEK, THE POOR MAN!
WE HAVE OUR MATINEE SHOW AT 2 O'CLOCK AND I NEED THIS MYSTERY FIXED QUICKLY!
WE WORK DURING OUR SCHOOL'S BIG BREAK -
SO WE'LL HAVE IT CLEARED UP BY 12.30!

12.08PM, 22 MINUTES TO GO.
WHO IS THAT MAN WITH THE PILOT'S HAT AND THE MONKEY?
MR VIVALDI SAID HIS NAME IS PHILEAS O'FLATHERTY-FOTHERINGAY, HE FLIES THE HOT AIR BALLOON THAT ADVERTISES THE CIRCUS. HIS CHIMP'S THE CO-PILOT.
COULD HE BE BEHIND THE TROUBLE?
NO, MR VIVALDI SAID HE AND THE MONKEY WERE 50 METRES IN THE AIR WHEN THE ACCIDENTS HAPPENED.
HMMMMM.
LET'S LOOK AT THE SCENE OF THE CRIME.
DO WE HAVE TO? YOU KNOW I DON'T LIKE CIRCUSES.
GIVE US A HUG!
FANCY SOME GRUB?
HOWEVER I'M SURE IN TIME I'LL LEARN TO LOVE THEM!
YUM! SAUSAGES!

THIS IS WHERE TINY THE ELEPHANT FELL.
STRANGE...
...IT TASTES LIKE BANANAS.
YES, YOU ARE STRANGE, LITTLE BROTHER.
LOOKS OKAY TO ME --
HOLD ON, WHAT'S THIS?
A BANANA PEEL!
WOULD YOU CARE FOR A LIQUORICE ALLSORT?
AHA! THIS COULD HAVE BEEN THE CAUSE OF THE MISFIRE –
A BANANA STUCK IN THE FUSE!
THAT CLINCHES IT, IT MUST HAVE BEEN PHILEAS AND HIS CHIMP!
BUT IT COULDN'T HAVE BEEN HIM, HE AND THE MONKEY WERE FLYING IN THE BALLOON, REMEMBER?
LOOK WHAT I FOUND IN THE HOT AIR BALLOON'S BASKET!
A MONKEY GLOVE PUPPET!
SO PHILEAS COULD HAVE BEEN UP IN THE BALLOON WITH THE PUPPET ON HIS ARM, LEAVING THE REAL MONKEY ON THE GROUND—

-- TO DO MY EVIL BIDDING!
YEAH, THAT'S RIGHT, I TRAINED THE MONKEY TO SABOTAGE THE CIRCUS, AND WORE THE GLOVE PUPPET IN THE BALLOON TO COVER HIS TRACKS!
PHILEAS!
BUT WHY DID YOU DO IT, MR. O'FLATHERTY-FOTHERINGAY?
I WAS SICK OF MY BEAUTIFUL BALLOON GETTING ONLY SECOND BILLING!
I HAD TO SABOTAGE VIVALDI'S CIRCUS -- NOBODY WANTS TO FLY IN A HOT AIR BALLOON WITH A FLEA BITTEN CHIMP WHEN THEY COULD BE WATCHING A TAP DANCING ELEPHANT!
??

MY LOVELY TINY?! YOU'LL NEVER GET AWAY WITH THIS!
OH YEAH? TRY AND STOP ME!
WOAH!
WE'VE...
...GOT...
...HIM!
NOOOOOO!
NOW, BENZINI BROTHERS, TO CATCH THIS BASKET CASE!

OOHYAH!
WOULD YOU CARE FOR A CANDIED PEANUT?
12.27PM, 3 MINUTES TILL THE END OF BIG BREAK.
WELL DONE DETECTIVES! YOU SAVED THE CIRCUS!
YOUR WHOLE CLASS IS INVITED TO THE MATINEE TODAY, AND FREE POPCORN FOR ALL!
WOW, THANKS MR VIVALDI!
...NOW, WE'D BETTER POP BACK TO SCHOOL AS QUICK AS WE CAN!
NEEE-NAAAAHH! NEEE-NAAAAHH!
TOMO
Now I love clowning around!
So I learned that I loved the circus, but hated bananas.
And after meeting Phileas O'Flatherty-Fotheringay, I realised that balloons are not the only things full of hot air!

THE HISTORY OF TELEVISION

An old–ish television

Teacher: Ms. Fallon
Student: Thomas Conway
Project: The History of Television

The television was invented in 1925 by Scottish inventor John Logie Baird, the genius who also introduced the trampoline to Tasmania.

Over the years the television (or teevee) has been used for educational, informational and entertainment–al purposes.

I love teevee. I love it more than computers, showers or toasters. Why do I love it so much, I hear you ask?

Three words: Hamm and Pickle.

Three more words: Masters of Disguise.

These are the two men that teevee was invented for. They are gods among teevee detectives.

Oh, there are plenty of detectives on teevee. There's Vespucci P.I., Destination: Homicide and the Miss Demeanor Adventures to name but three. But there's a huge difference between all those and Hamm and Pickle — they aren't masters of disguise!

When I hear the famous Hamm and Pickle theme tune, my mind drifts away to the mean streets of San Diego and to episode 26 of Season 3, "This Robot Squirrel is Sending Me Nuts and Bolts"...

Brock Gibbons IS SAMM HAMM
Salvatore Alonzo IS CONRAD PICKLE
IN
HAMM & PICKLE
MASTERS OF DISGUISE
© ROARING FERRET FEATURES MCMLXXXIV
KRACKLE!
FAST-FORWARD!
-- THE ROBOT SQUIRREL.
THE ONE WITH THE CHIP CONTAINING THE US NUCLEAR DEFENCE CODES?
THAT'S THE ONE. HE'S IN THIS GRAVEYARD SOMEWHERE.
KEEP YOUR EYES PEELED.

KRACKLE! FAST-FORWARD!
THE VOLGOVIANS! THEY'RE AFTER CHIPPY TOO!
WE'D BETTER--
KRACKLE!
CHEEP! CHEEP!
AHHH. ZE FAMOUS HAMM UNT PICKLE.
...ZE ROBOT SQUIRREL, IF YOU PLEASE.
NOT SO FAST, IGOR--
KRACKLE!

KRACKLE!
SO HAMM, YOU KNEW THE SQUIRREL HAD BEEN TAILED?
YES. THE VOLGOVIANS WERE NUTS TO THINK THEY WOULD GET AWAY WITH IT.
HA HA HA!
HOOPF! HOOPF!
CHEEP! CHEEP!
THE END
© ROARING FERRET FEATURES MCMLXXXIV
In conclusion, teevee is the most important invention ever.
There are 1 billion and a half teevee sets in the world, but only 128 episodes of Hamm and Pickle: Masters of Disguise over 3 seasons.
Fin
Une production de Thomas Conway
Ms. Fallon's Class
COLA

THE BIG BREAK DETECTIVES
THE CASE OF THE
INVISIBLE PENGUINS
AN

CASE THREE

THE CASE OF THE INVISIBLE PENGIONS

ZOO! ZOO!
ZOO!

Permission Slip

I hereby grant permission for my son/daughter to attend the waxworks / the zoo / the national art gallery on

Tuesday / **15th**, leaving by coach / train / tram

from the school at **10** am/pm and

returning to the school at **3** am/pm.

Signed: MY MUM

REMEMBER YOU ARE REPRESENTING LADY AGATHA'S SCHOOL.
BEST BEHAVIOUR IS EXPECTED AT ALL TIMES.

LADY AGATHA CHESTERTON'S
SCHOOL FOR
GIRLS & BOYS

I LOVE SCHOOL TRIPS!
WHAT DO YOU GUYS WANT TO DO FIRST?
WELL, I WOULD SAY SEE THE PENGUINS, BUT I KNOW TOM IS GOING TO SAY--
THE CAFÉ!
-- THE CAFÉ, SO CAFÉ FIRST.
ZOO

YOU KNOW BROTHER, IT'S LUCKY WE'RE AT THE ZOO...
BECAUSE YOU HAVE THE TABLE MANNERS OF A GORILLA.
HUHMH?
FANCY A BANANA?
ZOO
HELP!!
ZOO
JIM
OUR PENGUINS HAVE DISAPPEARED!!
ZOO
HUH?!
OUR CARD.
ZOO
WOULD YOU CARE FOR A JELLY SNAKE?
ZOO
THE BIG BREAK DETECTIVES
MYSTERIES SOLVED IN THIRTY MINUTES FREE OF CHARGE

MYSTERIES SOLVED IN 30 MINUTES? PERFECT -- PENGUIN FEEDING TIME IS IN 15 MINUTES AND THE MAYOR IS COMING TO SEE IT.
WE HAVE TO FIND MY LITTLE PENGUINS BY THEN!
ZOO
JIM
WE'RE ON THE CASE!
FEEDING TIME : 13 MINUTES
WELL...
STA

...WHERE ARE THEY?
IT DOESN'T LOOK LIKE THEY'RE HERE...
BUT PENGUINS DON'T JUST BECOME INVISIBLE.
DID THEY FLY OUT?
OH, TOM...
WE'D BETTER SEE WHAT PER-CEE SAYS.
DON'T THINK I DIDN'T HEAR THAT MASTER THOMAS.
FLY OUT INDEED...
PER-CAM
PENGUIN FACTS
• They spend most of their lives in water
• Their body is insulated with a thick layer of blubber that keeps them warm
• They can walk faster than humans
• They can hold their breath for about 20 minutes under water
• Penguins don't fly, they swim
• They are warm blooded like humans
• Penguins have short legs and no knees
• Some species have yellow feathers
• Male penguins take care of their chicks
• Penguins use sign language to communicate with each other
INFO
PRESS HERE

OKAY OKAY, I GET IT. THEY CAN'T FLY. SO HOW--
EEEEP!
WHAT WAS THAT?!
LOOK! DO YOU SEE SOMETHING?
AH... AH... AHHHHH...
...CHOOOOOO!
HUH?
CHOO!
CHOO!
AHHH...
AH CHOO!

FEEDING TIME : 8 MINUTES
IT'S FLOUR! THEY'RE COVERED IN FLOUR!
NO WONDER WE COULDN'T SEE THEM IN THE FAKE SNOW!
WOW, LOOK AT THIS!
AND THIS!
WHAT'S THIS?
A ROPE LADDER --
FLOUR
-- PAINTED WHITE SO WE CAN'T SEE IT AGAINST THE BACK WALL!
HMM. HOW LONG TILL FEEDING TIME?
SEVEN MINUTES.
OKAY BOYS, HERE'S WHAT WE DO...
ZOO

Now usually this is the time I'd turn to Hamm and Pickle to formulate some ingenious disguise.

But in this case Kate decided that we would rely on good old fashioned bakery skills.

And now?

All white...

Recipe

Ingredients -

- One bag flour
- One boy *(half baked)*

Method -

1. Stand still
2. Heavily coat in flour
3. Voilà! Magnifique!

Just like Mama used to make!

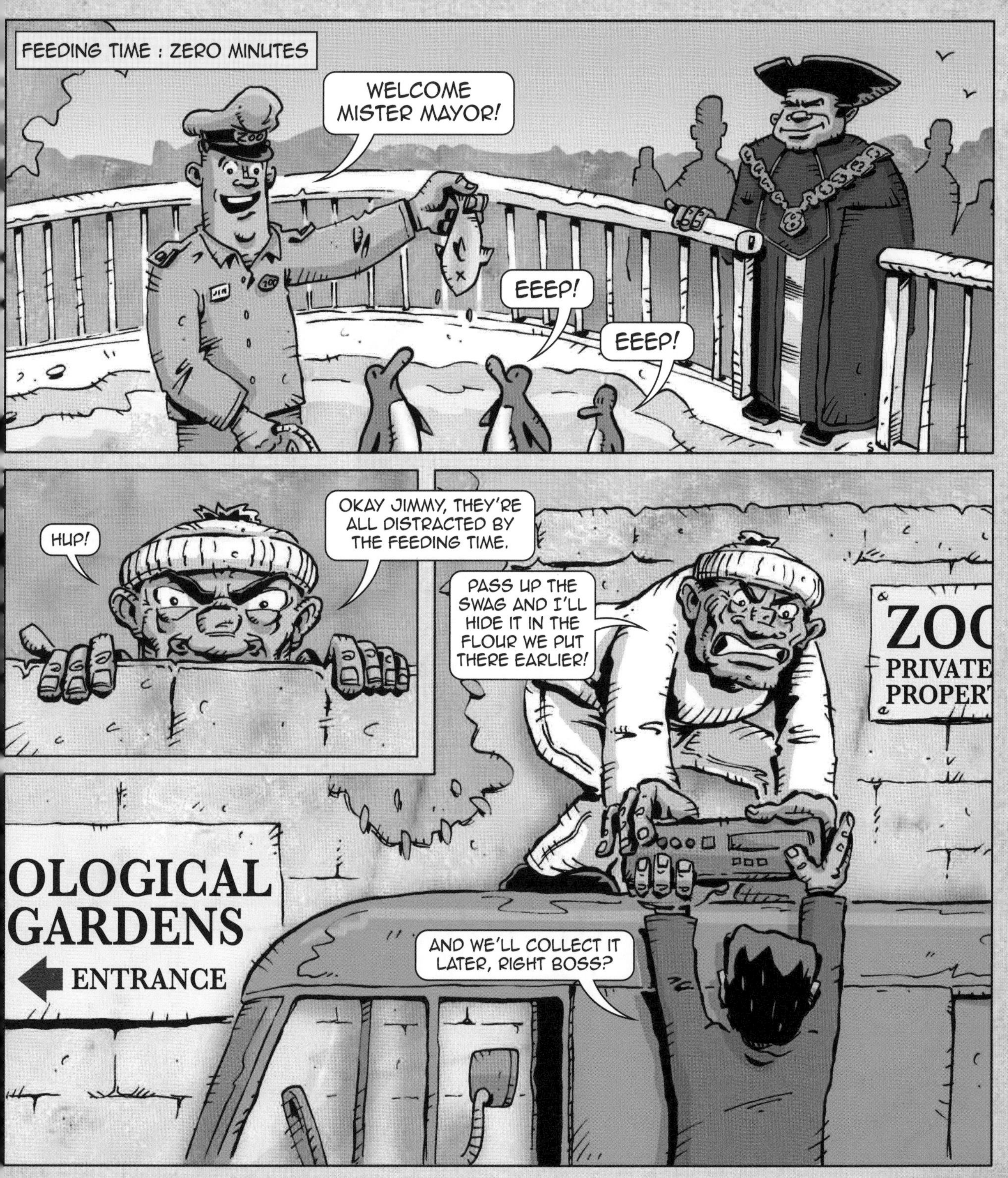

FEEDING TIME : ZERO MINUTES
WELCOME MISTER MAYOR!
ZOO
EEEP!
EEEP!
HUP!
OKAY JIMMY, THEY'RE ALL DISTRACTED BY THE FEEDING TIME.
PASS UP THE SWAG AND I'LL HIDE IT IN THE FLOUR WE PUT THERE EARLIER!
ZOO
PRIVATE
PROPERT
OLOGICAL
GARDENS
ENTRANCE
AND WE'LL COLLECT IT LATER, RIGHT BOSS?

WE SURE WILL, JIMMY. NO SAFER PLACE TO HIDE STOLEN GOODS THAN IN THE ZOO SURROUNDED BY WILD ANIMALS!
UNDER THE FLOUR YOU GO. I'LL BE BACK FOR YOU LATER, ME BEAUTIES!
NOT SO FAST!
AH CHOO!
WHA'?
ME LADDER! I CAN'T GET OUT!
WHAT'S WRONG?

-- YOU DIDN'T USE SELF RAISING FLOUR?!
WOULD YOU CARE FOR A SMALL-ISH FISH?
ZOO
WE'D BETTER GET BACK TO THE CAFÉ...
...AND FINISH OUR LUNCH FOR ONCE!

Relaxing with a good book.

Kate's 6th birthday – good times...

Danny, 6 months

What a bee-ootiful baba!

First disguise kit

ODE ON A BROKEN BLUEBOTTLE

Bluebottle, bluebottle buzzing about,
You buzz to the east and you buzz to the south,
You look so disgruntled,
I'll christen you Gerald,
And baptize you – SPLAT!
With last night's Daily Herald.

I bet he's GRUNTLED now.

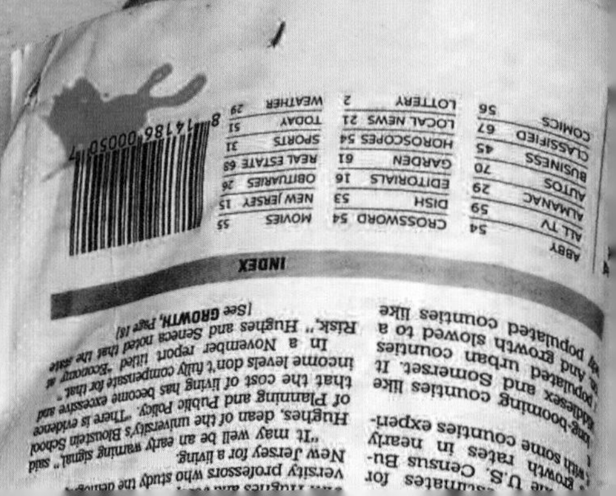

THE BIG BREAK DETECTIVES
THE CASE OF THE
PHANTOM LOLLIPOP LADY
CASE FOUR

THE CASE OF THE PHANTOM LOLLIPOP LADY

I have to get something off my chest: I don't believe in ghosts.

And even if they were real (which they're not) how could a ghost be scary? It's only made of fog or smoke or something like that.

I'm afraid of mice, but I'm not afraid of ghosts.

Okay, okay, I'm afraid of mice and spiders, and I used to be scared of clowns, but I'm not afraid of ghosts.

I'm not awfully fond of worms either.

Tarantula
Phylum: Arthropoda
Class: Arachnida

YUK

PICKLE
2.99
DISGUISE
NOSE (GREEN)

Hey check out my new fake nose!

ODE ON A BROKEN NOSE

Nose knows nothing, Nose knows all,
A nose so large, can make you fall.
Unions said "Picket",
And the workers went out,
Finger up nose, And wiggle it about.

LADY AGATHA'S SCHOOL, JUST BEFORE BIG BREAK.
BEEP! BEEP!
HONK! PARP!
WHAT'S WITH THESE CAR HORNS? THEY'RE BEEPING ALL DAY LONG!
TEACHER SAID THAT MOTORISTS HAVE BEEN COMPLAINING ABOUT A LOLLIPOP LADY THAT JUST APPEARS OUT OF NOWHERE AND STOPS THE TRAFFIC --
-- AND THEN *DISAPPEARS!*
HONK! PARP!
PARDON?
GATHER YE 'ROUND, CHILDREN, WHILE I TELL YE THE TALE OF THE *PHANTOM LOLLIPOP LADY.*
IN THE DISTANT MISTS OF TIME THERE WAS A LOLLIPOP LADY GOOD AND TRUE NAMED GOODY MERRIWEATHER, WHO DISAPPEARED UNDER MYSTERIOUS CIRCUM-STANCES, RIGHT OUTSIDE LADY AGATHA'S!
ONE DAY SHE WAS HERE, THE NEXT GONE. *POOF!* LIKE A PUFF OF SMOKE IN THE WIND.
IT SAYS HERE SHE RETIRED.
SSSSHHHH!

AND ONCE A YEAR HER SPIRIT IS SAID TO HAUNT THE ROAD OUTSIDE THE SCHOOL, HER LOLLIPOP IN HAND.
HALTING HORSES AND CARTS, HALTING CARS.
HALTING, HALTING, FOREVER HALTING...
IT'S THE HQ PHONE! SOMEONE NEEDS US!
GOOD TIMING!
THE BIG BREAK DETECTIVES ARE ON THE CASE!
BEEP! BEEP!
ULP.
12.02PM, 28 MINUTES LEFT.
PER CEE
IT'S FOR YOU.
I'M NOT YOUR PERSONAL SECRETARY, YOU KNOW.
HELLO?
SIR HORATIO FITZHUBERT OF RATHBREEN MANOR?
WE'LL BE RIGHT THERE!

12.05PM, 25 MINUTES TO GO.
...SO YOU SEE, THE DASHED NOISE FROM THE CAR HORNS IS DISTURBING MY MARROWS.
I WANTED TO ENTER THEM INTO THE FLOWER SHOW BEST VEGETABLE COMPETITION, BUT THEY ARE, AS YOU SEE, SOMEWHAT DEFLATED.
A PITY, I REALLY COULD HAVE DONE WITH THE PRIZE MONEY.
YOU SEE, THE OLD PILE HAS FALLEN INTO DISREPAIR, I'M AFRAID.
THE FITZHUBERTS USED TO BE QUITE WELL OFF BUT WE LOST OUR FORTUNE--
ON THE STOCK MARKET?
NO, GRANDPA FITZHUBERT WENT DOOLALLY AND HID ALL OUR JEWELLERY, INCLUDING GRANDMAMA'S PRICELESS *RUBY OF RANPOOR*, AND WE NEVER COULD FIND IT.
ALL THE OTHER PEERS ARE CALLING ME SIR HORATIO THREADBARE.

HONK! PARP!
BEEP! BEEP!
HELL'S TEETH! THERE THEY GO AGAIN! YOU'VE GOT TO HELP ME, CHILDREN!
RATHBREEN MANOR, 22 MINUTES TO GO.
HMMMM...
DANNY, DID YOU NOTICE THAT ALTHOUGH THE HOUSE IS FALLING APART, ONE THING LOOKS LIKE IT'S BEEN OILED RECENTLY?
SIR HORATIO'S HAIR?
NO TOM, THAT WASHING LINE. THE PULLEY IS OILED AND THE ROPE IS BRAND NEW AS WELL.
AND I DON'T THINK *THESE* BELONG TO SIR HORATIO...
SO LET'S PULL THE PULLEY!

HONK! PARP!
OH! THE CAR HORNS HAVE STARTED AGAIN!
THE ROPE GOES DOWN THROUGH THE TREES!
LET'S FOLLOW IT!
COAL
IT GOES RIGHT ACROSS THE MAIN ROAD...
AND LOOK! THE PHANTOM LOLLIPOP LADY!
HONK! PARP!
BEEP! BEEP!
PARP!
HOLD ON!

SHE'S NOT REAL! SHE'S MADE OF CARDBOARD AND ATTACHED BY STRINGS.
BEEP! BEEP!
PULL THE ROPE AGAIN DANNY!
HONK!
PARP!
GUNF!
WHIZZZZ!
BEEP! BEEP!
SO THE PHANTOM ISN'T A PHANTOM?
AWWW, MANNN.

SSSSHHHH!
WHAT'S THAT NOISE?
IT'S COMING FROM THE MANOR GROUNDS!
DDDDRRRRR! DDDDRRRRR!
SOUNDS LIKE IT'S COMING FROM THE COAL SHED.
THIEVES?
DDDDRRRRR! DDDDRRRRR!
DDDDRRRRR! DDDDRRRRR!
USING THE SOUND OF THE CAR HORNS--
TO DISGUISE THE SOUND OF THEIR JACKHAMMER DIGGING!
I HAVE AN IDEA!
SO DO I!

HAMM & PICKLE
MASTERS OF DISGUISE
NAME: Thomas Conway
MASTER OF DISGUISE GRADE 2
OFFICIAL FAN CLUB

Time to formulate a plan!

Pity I left my Hamm and Pickle fake nose at school...

RATHBREEN MANOR COAL SHED, 7 MINUTES TO GO.
OOOH MAMMY! I HEARD A NOISE!
SHUT UP, YOU BIG BABY.
BUT I'M SCARED OF THE PHANTOM LOLLIPOP LADY!
BUT THAT'S US, YOU DINGBAT!
OH YEAH.
DDDDRRRRRR! DDDDRRRRRR!
WOOOOOOOHHH! SSSSAFE TO CROSSSS NOW CHILDRENNNN!

KRASH!
MAMMY!
SHE'S REAL!
OOOYAH!
WHAT'S THIS?
AN OLD MAP OF RATHBREEN MANOR?
WITH AN X-MARKS-THE-SPOT!
WHAT ARE THEY DIGGING FOR?
NOT TELLING.
THE RUBY OF RANPOOR!
SHUT UP, DINGBAT!
LEAVE THIS TO ME --
I *DIG* DIGGING!
DDDDRRRRR! DDDDRRRRR
A SAFE!
THE RUBY!

THE RUBY OF RANPOOR, FOUND AT LAST!
WELL DONE, CHILDREN, YOU HAVE SAVED RATHBREEN MANOR... AND MY MARROWS!
AND YOU'VE CAUGHT THESE TWO -- WE'VE BEEN AFTER THEM FOR MONTHS!
WOULD YOU CARE FOR A CARROT?
UH OH! LOOK AT THE TIME.
WE'VE GOT TO GET BACK TO SCHOOL!
YEAH! TIME OUR CLASSMATES MET THE REAL PHANTOM LOLLIPOP LADY!

Well that's it. Sir Horatio sold the ruby, fixed his house up, and also bought a tuck shop for the school!

Unfortunately it doesn't sell sweets, just organic vegetables that he grows himself in Rathbreen Manor.

Hooray.

Wow, I'm nearly out of paper!

I'm glad Kate asked me to keep this journal. It's been fun to write down about all the great times me, Danny and Kate have during Big Break at Lady Agatha's.

And PER–CEE too of course.

I must go down to the HQ and oil him sometime... You never know when we might need him again!

DIXIE
MY DAD...

Original sketch for the Big Break Detectives

Alan Nolan lives and works in Bray, County Wicklow, Ireland. He is co-creator (with Ian Whelan) of SANCHO comic which was shortlisted for two Eagle awards, and is writer and illustrator of the SKREWY SCIENCE WITH PROF. BUTTERKNUT & KRONK cartoon strip for the *Irish Times*. He the author and illustrator of two books in the 'Murder Can Be Fatal' series: *Death By Chocolate* and *Six Million Ways To Die* (The O'Brien Press).

Special thanks to Mary, Michael, Emma, Ivan and all at The O'Brien Press, Ian, Paul, Garvan, Mark, Dave, Mark B, Aidan and RíRá, and Rachel.

www.BigBreakDetectives.com

www.alannolan.ie

www.obrien.ie